The Flamingo Flap

'The Flamingo Flap'
An original concept by Jill Atkins
© Jill Atkins

Illustrated by Kelly Breemer

Published by MAVERICK ARTS PUBLISHING LTD
Studio 3A, City Business Centre, 6 Brighton Road,
Horsham, West Sussex, RH13 5BB
© Maverick Arts Publishing Limited May 2019
+44 (0)1403 256941

A CIP catalogue record for this book is available at the British Library.

ISBN 978-1-84886-442-9

www.maverickbooks.co.uk

Yellow

This book is rated as: Yellow Band (Guided Reading)
This story is decodable at Letters and Sounds Phase 3/4.

The Flamingo Flap

by Jill Atkins

illustrated by Kelly Breemer

The flamingos were looking
for fish in the pool.

"We need a bigger pool with a lot of fish," said the big flamingo.

All the flamingos took off.

But Flick had hurt her wing.

"I am in a flap," she said.

"I cannot go."

"I will wait for you," said Flash.

"My wing hurts," said Flick.

"Then we will go on foot," said Flash.

Tap!

They set off.

But soon Flash hurt his foot.

"We can hop to the big pool,"
said Flick.

Hop!

They set off.

Flap, flap!

"My wing feels a bit better," said Flick.

Flap, flap!

"My wing feels
a lot better," she said.

Flick and Flash took off.

"Look!" said Flick.

"I can see the big pool."

"It is good to see you!"

said the big flamingo.

"You can join our party."

"It is the Flamingo Flap!"

Quiz

1. Where are the flamingos going?
a) A wood
b) The sea
c) The big pool

2. What are they looking for in the pool?
a) Fish
b) Frogs
c) Weeds

3. What has Flick hurt?
a) Her foot
b) Her wing
c) Her head

4. "We can _____ to the big pool."
a) Run
b) Flap
c) Hop

5. What is the party called?
a) The Flamingo Flap
b) The Hopping Flamingo
c) The Flamingo Flick

Turn over for answers

Book Bands for Guided Reading

Pink

Red

Yellow

Blue

Green

Orange

Turquoise

Purple

Gold

White

The Institute of Education book banding system is a scale of colours that reflects the various levels of reading difficulty. The bands are assigned by taking into account the content, the language style, the layout and phonics.

Maverick Early Readers are a bright, attractive range of books covering the pink to white bands. All of these books have been book banded for guided reading to the industry standard and edited by a leading educational consultant.

To view the whole Maverick Readers scheme, visit our website at

www.maverickearlyreaders.com

Or scan the QR code above to view our scheme instantly!

Quiz Answers: 1c, 2a, 3b, 4c, 5a